(WELLINGTON SQUAI

Clever dog!

Keith Gaines

Rocky was watching television.
'Is it good?' asked Rocky's mother.
'Yes,' said Rocky.
'What's it about?' asked his mother.
'Those three prisoners have
broken out of the prison.
One of them has a gun.
They are running across a field.
Lots of other people are trying to
catch them with police dogs.'

Rocky's mother went out to make a cup of tea.
'Would you like to be a police dog?'
she asked Max.
'Woof!' said Max.
'Would you like to run after prisoners?'
'Woof, woof!' said Max.

Rocky's mother came back in with the tea on a tray.
Rocky hadn't moved.
'Have they caught them yet?'
asked Rocky's mother.
'They have caught the burglar,' said Rocky,
'and they have caught the burglar's friend,
but the mad killer is in that shed with the gun
and the police are all around.'
The man on the TV was shouting,
'You won't put me back in prison!'

4

Just try and get me, you rats!

The first one through that door is a dead man!

Ow!
He got me!

Are you OK?

He got me in the arm.
It's bleeding and it hurts,
but I think it'll be OK.

We'd better get
you to a doctor.

That can wait!
I'm not going in an ambulance, and
I'm not going in a hospital ward...

...until he's behind bars.
Let the dogs catch him!

Woof! Woof!

You would never have got me without the dogs, you rat!

I would have killed all of you, if I could...

...but dogs are my favourite animals.

13

I just couldn't hurt a dog!

14

Take him away!

15

You know, I believe there's some good in everyone!

16

'That was brilliant!' said Rocky.

'Finish your tea and get to bed,' said his mother.

'You'll be tired if you stay up any longer.'

'But it's Saturday tomorrow,' said Rocky.

'I don't have to get up for school.'

'Get to bed!' said his mother.

The next day, Rocky and Max were in the park.
'I'm going to train you,' said Rocky.
'I'm going to train you to be as clever
as those dogs on TV last night.
First, you have to bring this ball back to me.
Are you ready?'
'Woof!' said Max.
Rocky showed Max the ball.
'Keep your eye on the ball,' said Rocky.

'Go and get it, Max!' said Rocky.
Max ran off as quickly as he could.
He raced back to Rocky with the ball.
'Well done, Max. Clever dog,' said Rocky.
'Now see if you can get this stick.'

Max ran after the stick.

He picked it up and brought it back to Rocky.

'Good dog!' said Rocky. 'Clever dog!'

As Rocky was picking up the stick,

Max suddenly ran off.

He came back with a small branch.

He dropped the branch at Rocky's feet.

'What's this?' asked Rocky, but

Max had run off again.

'What is Max doing?' thought Rocky.
Max was running to the trees near the pond.
A minute later Max came back and
dropped a big branch at Rocky's feet.
'I don't want this,' said Rocky.
But Max had run off again.
This time he came back with two big branches!
'Stop!' said Rocky, as Max ran off again.
'I don't want any more.
No more branches!'

When Max came back, he didn't have a branch –
he had a kite!
As Max dropped the kite at Rocky's feet,
Jamila and Wing Chan came running up to Rocky.
'We were flying our kites,' said Jamila.
'When my kite dipped down near the ground,
Max jumped up and grabbed it.'
'Sorry about that,'
said Rocky, as he gave the kite back.
'It looks OK,' said Jamila. 'I don't think it's broken.'

'I think we'd better do another sort of training,'
said Rocky.
Rocky took Max around to the back of the shed.
'You stay here. Down, boy, down!'
Max lay flat on the ground.
'I'll be back in a minute,' said Rocky.
Rocky ran off with the ball.

Rocky came back.

'Now you go and find the ball,' Rocky said to Max.

Max did not move.

'Come on, Max,' said Rocky.

'I'm asking you to find the ball.

Go and get it!'

Max ran out from behind the shed.
He was not sure what to look for
and he did not know where to look.
Max looked around the park.
Should he look around the swings,
or should he look around the pond?

Can you help Max to find Rocky's ball?
If you want Max to look around the swings, go to p 18.
If you want Max to look around the pond, go to p 19.

Max ran over to the swings and looked around.
A minute later Max ran back to Rocky.
Max dropped something and Rocky picked it up.
'Oh, no!' said Rocky. 'It's an old banana!
It looks as if someone dropped
this about a week ago!
I will have to put it in the dustbin.
Go and look for my ball.
You could look around the pond.
You could look around the flowers,
or you could look around near the gate.'

If you want Max to look around the pond, go to p 19.
If you want Max to look around the flowers, go to p 20.
If you want Max to look around near the gate, go to p 21.

Max ran over to the pond and looked around.
All he could see was water, some mud and
some pond weed.
Max ran back to Rocky.
Max dropped something and Rocky picked it up.
'Oh, no! It's a lot of weeds!' said Rocky.
He looked at the weeds. 'They're all wet,
and there's a big black beetle in them!
I will have to put this back in the pond.
Go and look for my ball.
You could look around the swings.
You could look around the flowers,
or you could look around near the gate.'

If you want Max to look around the swings, go to p 18.
If you want Max to look around the flowers, go to p 20.
If you want Max to look around near the gate, go to p 21.

Max ran over to the flowers.
He had just found something when
Fred shouted at him.
'Those flowers weren't put there for dogs.
Go away!'
Max ran back to Rocky.
Max dropped something and Rocky picked it up.
'Oh! This is the sort of switch you get on radios!'
said Rocky. 'It might have come off Kevin's
radio, when it got blown up.
It's all rusty now.
Come on, let's put this in the dustbin,
and I'll show you where the ball is.'

Go to p 22.

Max ran over to the gate and looked around.
A minute later Max ran back to Rocky.
'That doesn't look like my ball,' said Rocky.
Max dropped something and Rocky picked it up.
'Oh, no! It's a dead frog!' said Rocky.
'You can't put frogs that have died
back into a pond.
Come on, let's leave this here on the ground,
and I'll show you where the ball is.'

Go to p 22.

Rocky took Max over to the statue of
the Duke of Wellington.
Fred was walking over to the statue too.
He had a big ladder.
'What's the ladder for?' asked Rocky.
'Hello, Rocky,' said Fred.
'I thought it was time the Duke and
his horse had a little clean.
The old Duke believed in keeping clean, you know.'

Go to p 23.

'I've been watching you playing with your dog,' said Fred.

'What are you trying to do with him?'

'I'm trying to train him to find stuff,' said Rocky.

'But he's not very good at it.

Look, Max. Here is where I put the ball.

It's under this bench.'

Rocky reached under the bench to get the ball.

Go to p 24.

23

'Here it is,' said Rocky.
'But there's another thing here, too.
I didn't see this before.
It's stuck at the back of the bench.'
Rocky pulled it out.
'It's a little bag,' said Rocky.
'I don't think I know anyone who
owns a bag like this.
Do you, Fred?'
'Let me just lean my ladder on the Duke,' said Fred.
'Then I'll have a look.'

Go to p 25.

'No,' said Fred.

'I can't remember anyone coming into the park with
a bag like that.

See if there's anything inside it.'

Rocky opened the little bag.

'There's some money inside,' said Rocky.

'There's quite a lot of money –
and there's a necklace.

There are two little nets,
but there's no name in here.'

Go to p 26.

Fred looked at the necklace.

'I'm sure I've seen that necklace before,' he said.

'But I can't remember where.'

'What should I do with it?' asked Rocky.

'You'd better give it to PC Kent or WPC Clark the next time you see one of them,' said Fred.

'What are these for?' asked Rocky, as he showed Fred the two little nets.

Go to p 27.

Fred looked at one of the nets.

'Not many people have nets like this these days,' he said. 'At one time lots of people had them. You would put a net over your head at night. It's the sort of thing an old lady might have.'

Fred looked at the necklace again.

'I know I've seen that necklace before,' he said. 'Who could have a necklace like that?'

Go to p 28.

'I think it must be a lady,' said Rocky.
'It may be a lady who lives in Wellington Square.
But there are lots of them!
How can we find out who left the bag here?'
'Woof! Woof!' said Max suddenly.
'What is it, Max?' said Rocky.
'Do you know who owns the necklace?'
'Woof!' said Max.
'Go on, then,' said Rocky.
'Show me the lady who owns the necklace!'

Have you seen the necklace before?
Who do you think owns the necklace?
Who do you think left the bag in the park?

If you want Max to go to Mrs Valentine, go to p 29.
If you want Max to go to Mrs Patel, go to p 30.
If you want Max to go to Mrs Miller, go to p 31.
If you want Max to go to Mrs Nash, go to p 32.

Max ran to the house where Mrs Valentine lives.
She was in the garden.
'Hello, Mrs Valentine,' said Rocky.
'Is this your necklace?'
'That stupid chimp next door is always
trying to steal my necklace,' said Mrs Valentine.
'But right now it's safe in my drawer upstairs.

It wasn't Mrs Valentine who had left the bag in the park.
If you want Max to go to Mrs Patel, go to p 30.
If you want Max to go to Mrs Miller, go to p 31.
If you want Max to go to Mrs Nash, go to p 32.

Max ran to the shop.
Rocky opened the door.
'Hello, Mr Patel,' said Rocky.
'Is this Mrs Patel's necklace?'
'I don't think so,' said Jamila's Dad.
'Just a minute. I'll find out.'
Mr Patel went into the back of the
shop for a minute.
'No, it isn't,' he said when he came back.
'Now get that dog out of my shop!'

It wasn't Mrs Patel who had left the bag in the park.
If you want Max to go to Mrs Valentine, go to p 29.
If you want Max to go to Mrs Miller, go to p 31.
If you want Max to go to Mrs Nash, go to p 32.

Max ran to Kevin's house.
Kevin and Rick were mending a car.
'Hello, Kevin,' said Rocky.
'Does your Mum own this necklace?'
'I don't think so,' said Kevin.
'Just a minute. I'll find out.'
Rocky heard Kevin's Mum shouting,
'No, and I don't want you or your
brother to bring any more mess into the house!'

It wasn't Mrs Miller who had left the bag in the park.
If you want Max to go to Mrs Valentine, go to p 29.
If you want Max to go to Mrs Patel, go to p 30.
If you want Max to go to Mrs Nash, go to p 32.

Max ran to the house where Mrs Nash lives.
Mrs Nash looked through the window.
Then Rocky waited as she opened her front door.
'Hello, Mrs Nash,' said Rocky.
'Is this your necklace?'
'Yes, it is!' said Mrs Nash. 'Where did you find it?'
When Rocky told her, she said,
'I always sit down on that bench when
I walk across the park.
My little bag must have dropped through
the bench when I put it down.
How clever of you to find it. I've looked all over for it.
It's a lovely necklace. I've had it for so many years.
How did you know it was *my* necklace?'
'It was Max who did it,' said Rocky.
'Max is better than a police dog!'

The end